External auditing

Workbook

John Taylor

osborne
BOOKS

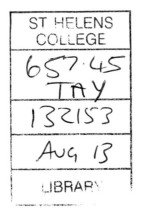
Published by Osborne Books Limited
Unit 1B Everoak Estate
Bromyard Road
Worcester WR2 5HP
Tel 01905 748071
Email books@osbornebooks.co.uk
Website www.osbornebooks.co.uk

Design by Laura Ingham
Cover and page design image © Istockphoto.com/Petrovich9

Printed by CPI Antony Rowe, Chippenham and Eastbourne

British Library Cataloguing in Publication Data
A catalogue record for this book is available from the British Library

ISBN 978 1905777 556

Contents

Chapter activities

Chapter activities – answers

Practice assessments

Practice assessments – answers

Acknowledgements

The authors wish to thank the following for their help with the reading and production of the book: Maz Loton, Jon Moore, Jo Osborne and Cathy Turner.

The publisher is indebted to the Association of Accounting Technicians for its kind permission to reproduce sample practice assessment material.

Thanks are also due to Laura Ingham for her designs for this new series.

Author

John Taylor is a Chartered Accountant who spent many years in professional practice, advising small and medium-sized businesses before becoming the Financial Director of a Leeds based public limited company. In 2004 John joined the staff of Leeds Metropolitan University, where he specialises in teaching management accounting and auditing on a range of professional courses.

Introduction

what this book covers

This book has been written specifically for the Learning Area 'External Auditing' which covers two QCF Units in the AAT Level 4 Diploma in Accounting:

■ Principles of external audit

■ Auditing financial statements

what this book contains

This book is set out in two sections:

■ **Chapter activities** which provide extra practice material in addition to the activities included in the Osborne Books Tutorial text. Answers to the Chapter activities are set out in this book.

■ **Practice Assessments** are included to prepare the student for the Computer Based Assessments. They are based directly on the structure, style and content of the sample assessment material provided by the AAT at www.aat.org.uk. Suggested answers to the Practice Assessments are set out in this book.

online support from Osborne Books

This book is supported by practice material available at www.osbornebooks.co.uk

This material is available to tutors – and to students at their discretion – in two forms:

■ A **Tutor Zone** which is available to tutors who have adopted the Osborne Books texts. This area of the website provides extra assessment practice material (plus answers) in addition to the activities included in this Workbook text.

■ **E-learning** – online practice questions designed to familiarise students with the style of the AAT Computer Based Assessments.

further information

If you want to know more about our products, please visit www.osbornebooks.co.uk, email books@osbornebooks.co.uk or telephone Osborne Books Customer Services on 01905 748071.

Chapter activities

1 Chapter activities
Introduction to auditing

1.1 From the list below select which of these statements best describes the reason why auditors should be independent of their clients.

		✓
(a)	They can charge larger fees as independent consultants	
(b)	The government insists auditors must be independent	
(c)	It enables them to carry out their audit without being influenced by their client	
(d)	Auditors are required to contribute to control procedures designed to detect fraud	

1.2 Which of the following statements about the role of the auditor is true?

		True	False
(a)	The role of the auditor is to prepare and express an opinion on the truth and fairness of a set of financial statements		
(b)	The role of the auditor is to express an opinion to the shareholders on the truth and fairness of a set of financial statements		
(c)	Auditors are responsible for detecting fraud in a set of financial statements		
(d)	The role of the auditor is to express an opinion to the directors on the truth and fairness of a set of financial statements		

1.3   State whether the following statements are true or false.

✓

		True	*False*
(a)	The auditor has to obtain reasonable assurance that the financial statements are true and fair		
(b)	Directors are responsible for the organisation's system of internal control which should be capable of detecting significant fraud or error		
(c)	The auditors are appointed until the end of the Annual General Meeting when they can be reappointed by the directors		
(d)	Any qualified accountant can apply to be registered as an auditor		

1.4   Who appoints the auditors?

✓

(a)	The Registrar of Companies	
(b)	An Audit Committee of non-executive directors	
(c)	The Board of Directors	
(d)	The members of the company	

2 Chapter activities
Auditing – the legal framework

2.1 State whether the following statements are true or false in respect of the liability of auditors.

✓

		True	False
(a)	Auditors are only responsible to shareholders		
(b)	Auditors have a duty of care towards investors or potential investors they are aware of before they sign the auditor's report		
(c)	Auditors owe a duty of care to each individual investor they are aware of before they sign the auditor's report		

2.2 Complete the following description of quality control procedures by filling in the gaps with terms from the list below:

- ▮ Regular
- ▮ Hot
- ▮ Cold
- ▮ Quality
- ▮ Ethical
- ▮ Independence
- ▮ Audit
- ▮ Reviewed
- ▮ Simple
- ▮ Complex

All audit firms must have a system of . . . . control. This should include confirmation

that . . . . standards have been maintained, that the firm's . . . . from

the client has not been compromised, that all audit work carried out has been reviewed and that the

client continues to be acceptable. A . . . . review should take place where the audit

is large or. . . . . and a system of . . . . reviews implemented to ensure

the firms audit procedures have been adhered to.

2.3   State whether the following statements are true or false in respect of the rights of auditors.

✓

	True	False
(a) Auditors have the right to be present at the Annual General Meeting		
(b) Auditors have the right to have all reasonable inquiries answered		
(c) Auditors have the right to attend all meetings of the company		
(d) Auditors have the right to inspect any information including information not related to the financial records, for example, personnel files		
(e) Auditors have the right to call an Annual General Meeting		

2.4   Auditors can minimise their liability to third parties in several ways.

State whether the following ways for auditors to minimise their liability is allowed or not allowed under the ethical guidelines.

✓

	Allowed	Not allowed
Auditors can include a disclaimer in their report to disclaim all liability for loss as the directors are responsible for the content		
Audit firms can operate as companies with limited liability		
Audit firms can make agreements with individual shareholders and repay any losses they have incurred in the hope that not all shareholders will claim		
Auditors can include a disclaimer on their accounts to disclaim all liability for loss in respect of any third party apart from the shareholders		
Audit firms can agree a maximum amount of liability with the directors and shareholders of a client		

3 Chapter activities
Planning the audit assignment

3.1 Match each of the control activities/procedures listed below with the appropriate type of internal control shown in the table.

Control activity/procedure:

- Staff responsible for recording cash received are not responsible for processing sales invoices
- Supervisory responsibilities clearly defined
- A requirement for two signatures on all company cheques
- Matching of sales invoices to delivery notes and original sales order
- Limited access and password protection to the payroll system

Internal control:	Control activity/procedure:
Segregation of duties	
Physical control	
Arithmetical and accounting checks	
Organisational controls	
Authorisation controls	

3.2   When planning their audit the auditors must consider audit risk and the probability of a material misstatement or error not being detected by the company's procedures.

Select whether the following factors are likely to increase/reduce or have no effect on audit risk.

✓

		Increase	Reduce	No effect
a)	The company exceeds its overdraft limit every month			
b)	The company has introduced a bonus scheme for directors based on achieving revenue and profit targets			
c)	The company has upgraded its payroll software			
d)	Another firm of accountants has been approached to carry out internal audit reviews			
e)	The audit manager has joined the company as financial director			

3.3   Accounting systems should be designed with both control objectives and control procedures. Control procedures are designed to reduce the risk that control objectives are not met.

For each of the items below identify whether it is a control objective, a risk, or a control procedure.

✓

	Control objective	Risk	Control procedure
An aged receivables analysis is prepared monthly			
Invoices can be paid before goods are delivered			
Goods are only purchased from approved suppliers			
The payroll department is notified of starters and leavers by the personnel office			
The person responsible for collecting cash from vending machines pays the cash into the bank and notifies the cashiers department of the amount collected			

3.4   When documenting clients' systems auditors are concerned with identifying which accounting systems will be subject to audit procedures.

Glitterball Ltd manufactures jewellery for the fashion accessories market. It uses designs from independent designers and produces items in bulk for the cheaper jewellery high street retailers and accessory shops. It does not sell to the public.

Which of Glitterball's systems will *not* be subject to detailed audit procedures?

		✓
(a)	Purchases and supplier payments	
(b)	Inventory despatch and invoicing	
(c)	Payroll standard cost analysis	
(d)	Receivables and cash recording	

Chapter activities

Audit testing

4

4.1 Auditors use a mixture of tests of control and substantive procedures when gathering audit evidence.

For each of the procedures below indicate whether it is test of control, or a substantive procedure.

✓

	Test of control	Substantive procedure
Carry out analytical review of payables (creditors) ledger balances		
Test a sample of purchase orders for authorisation		
Reperform the bank reconciliation at year end		
Look for evidence that goods are despatched only to credit worthy customers		
Check authorisation for new employees details added to payroll		

4.2 Auditors use sampling as part of their auditing procedures.

You are reviewing the audit programme for the audit of Bolington Ltd. The audit programme sets out the following audit tests:

From the information given decide if the test is valid or not valid.

✓

		Valid	Not valid
(a)	Select a sample of sales invoices and credit notes and vouch with goods outwards documents		
(b)	At the inventory count identify a selection of items to be counted independently by the audit team		
(c)	To test payroll transactions check all entries in week 23		
(d)	Using random number tables select a sample of goods received notes and check to purchase invoices		

4.3   Auditors must document their procedures and have evidence that they have planned their audit and carried out sufficient testing to support their audit opinion. All their work must be documented.

From the information below decide if the documentation should be retained on the Permanent Audit file or Current Audit file.

✓

	Current file	Permanent file
Audit points forward from prior years		
Schedule of additions to fixed assets		
Copy of the client's customer list		
Analytical comparison of results for previous five accounting periods		
List of employees authorised to sign purchase orders and their authorisation limits		

4.4   An external auditor is required to carry out audit testing to gather evidence to support their conclusions.

Select whether each of the statements below is true or false.

✓

		True	False
(a)	The principle of substance over form means that auditors will examine what a transaction really is not what it appears to be		
(b)	Auditors must use sampling to test every aspect of the financial statements when auditing a large company		
(c)	Auditors should not attempt to develop a working relationship with client staff as this might compromise their independence		
(d)	Tolerable misstatement is the level of error the auditors will accept in a sample and is set lower than performance materiality		

Chapter activities
5 Auditing accounting systems

5.1 As part of their audit work auditors will seek to verify the assertions relevant to the transactions being audited.

You are carrying out the audit of a payroll system. For each of the audit procedures set out below select the assertion for which the test will provide assurance.

Test	Assertion
Check sample of new employees details with personnel records	Existence/Classification/Accuracy/Occurrence
Check calculation of a sample of gross pay for hourly paid employees	Occurrence/Valuation/Classification/Accuracy
Reconcile the wages control account	Cut off/Valuation/Classification/ Occurrence

5.2 Two types of computer-assisted audit techniques (CAAT) are test data and audit software.

For each of the audit procedures listed below, select the type of CAAT which would be used to perform that procedure.

	Test data	Audit software
Stratification of ledger balances to provide data for sampling tests		
Input employee salary data to generate predicted payroll figures		
Identify any gaps in the sequence of sales invoice number		

5.3 The following is a description of a payroll system within Skye Ltd.

For each part of the system identify whether the procedure is a strength or a weakness or is neither a strength nor a weakness.

✓

	Strength	Neither	Weakness
(a) Each hourly paid employee is required to swipe an electronic card which records the time they enter and leave the premises. There is no supervision of this procedure.			
(b) Each departmental manager receives a printout of their employees recorded hours on the last day of the pay period and is required to initial to approve payment of those hours.			
(c) Information from the swipe card machine is downloaded automatically into the payroll programme. The payroll clerk can amend this manually where a manager has refused to authorise hours worked.			
(d) The payroll clerk can also amend monthly paid employee's pay details and all employee's deductions maintained in the payroll master file.			
(e) The Human Resources department sends an e-mail detailing new starters and employees leaving to the payroll supervisor who is responsible for ensuring that all new employees' details are input into the master file and that all leavers are removed from the payroll after their final salary payment.			
(f) A BACS payment list is prepared from the payroll details and sent to the Financial Director for approval. She signs it and has it countersigned by the Financial Controller.			
(g) All employees are paid by electronic transfer.			
(h) The payroll department sends a monthly e-mail to the accounts department showing the amounts of PAYE and NI required to be paid to HM Revenue & Customs.			

5.4   Auditors use both substantive and compliance testing as part of their audit procedures.

For each of the tests described below decide whether or not it is a test of control or a substantive test.

✓

	Test of control	Substantive procedure
Check for evidence that supplier's accounts in the Payables Ledger are reconciled monthly to the statement from the supplier		
Check for evidence that purchase invoices are batched before being input into the financial records and that batch details are recorded		
Check that the numerical sequence of Goods Returned Notes is unbroken		
Check that staff leaving employment are removed from the payroll promptly		
Physically inspect a sample of motor vehicles and record details		

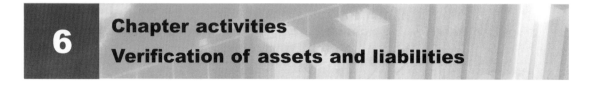

6 Chapter activities
Verification of assets and liabilities

6.1 An external auditor is required to carry out audit testing to gather evidence to support their conclusions.

Select whether each of the statements below is true or false.

		True	False
(a)	If the bank reconciliation is correct there is no need for a separate confirmation letter from the bank		
(b)	Inspecting non current assets is a valid test for existence and ownership		
(c)	Research expenditure can be capitalised as a tangible non-current asset but must be written off within five years		
(d)	Carrying out a trade receivables circularisation will provide some good evidence of existence and valuation of receivables balances		

6.2   The following is a description of an inventory count within Whisper Ltd.

For each part of the system identify whether the procedure is a strength or a weakness.

	Strength	Weakness
(a) The count is to be carried out by Whisper staff in teams of two.		
(b) One person will count the inventory item and the other will record the count on a pad. Counters should bring a pad and pens for this purpose		
(c) Once counted each item should be marked with a red sticker. If teams run out of red stickers they are able to use the green ones also		
(d) The stores area has been organised into sections and each team will be allocated to a section to count		
(e) The stores staff will oversee the count and allocate teams to each area		
(f) Teams should inspect each inventory item for evidence of damage. Damaged stock should be noted separately by each team		
(g) Where inventories are boxed count staff are empowered to require stores staff to open a sample of the boxes to confirm the contents		
(h) Members of the audit team will be observing the counting of inventories. They will perform their own count of a sample of items and will record them separately. Count teams must not use the auditors as additional counters.		
(i) Once the count is complete the count sheets should be left with Mr Brown the Stores manager who will forward them to the finance department.		

6.3   All audit working papers must be reviewed during the course of the audit.

You are the audit manager of Tickett & Wrunne and you are reviewing the audit working papers on the current audit of Snodgrass Ltd. The audit team has created a list of queries on which they would like a decision from you.

Pre tax profit is £2.4M and the auditors have set a level of performance materiality at 5% of pre tax profits

- A provision for a loss on a long term contract has been omitted amounting to £50,000. The total value of inventories is £5m.

- The company has failed to make a provision against a receivables balance which may not be recoverable. The auditors calculate that it should be £25,000. The total value of trade receivables is £695,000.

- The company has classified £2.5m of leased property as freehold property.

- Expenditure on research should be written off in the year. Instead the company has upheld, as an intangible non current asset, research expenditure amounting to £15,000 claiming it is in respect of a potential future product.

You are asked to consider which is the right course of action for you to take when discussing these points with the client:

		✓
(a)	All the adjustments are material so all should be adjusted	
(b)	None of the adjustments are material so none need to be adjusted	
(c)	The provision against the contract in progress must be made and the property reclassified but no other adjustment need be made	
(d)	Only the provision against the work in progress needs to be amended	
(e)	The total of the errors exceeds performance materiality so all must be adjusted	

6.4   The external auditor should undertake analytical procedures as part of the planning process in order to identify the risk of misstatement of figures in the financial statements. The results of the analytical procedures conducted on trade receivables and trade payables in the financial statements of an audit client are listed below.

Select whether the results indicate that trade receivables and trade payables might have been under or overstated.

The results show that, compared to the previous year:

■   Trade receivables have increased by 5% and revenue has increased by 15%

Understated / Overstated

■   Trade payables have increased by 9% and purchases have decreased by 12%

Understated / Overstated

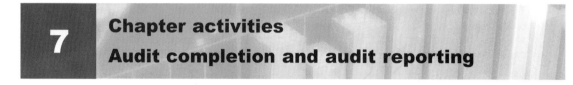

Chapter activities

7　Audit completion and audit reporting

7.1　You are reviewing the audit files of Monty Ltd with a view to finalising the audit. From your review of the files you identify the following factors . Identify whether or not they:

(a)　can be ignored

(b)　require the financial statements to be amended

(c)　require a note in the financial statements, without any adjustment to the figures

In the table below tick the response you feel is the most appropriate.

✓

	Ignore	Amend financial statements	Include in a note
(a) A customer owing £130,000 has gone into liquidation after the year end and no amounts will be recovered. Total receivables amount to £1.8m and the pre tax profit for the year is £750,000			
(b) Since the year end the company issued shares to the value of £1m			
(c) Audit investigations have indicated that the latest position on one of the long term contracts in progress is that it is likely to make a profit of £200,000. The contract is approximately 70% completed. The value of long-term work in progress is £5.0m and the pre tax profit for the year is £750,000			
(d) The bank financing arrangements were revised and renewed shortly after the year end. There were no changes to previous arrangements except an increase in the overdraft limit of £500,000			
(e) The company had revalued its freehold properties in line with general increases in market prices but during the year the value of commercial properties fell. The auditors estimate that these properties are overvalued by approximately £300,000			
(f) After the year end the main factory burned down causing a complete halt to production. The company arranged for production to be carried out by sub-contractors whilst the factory was being rebuilt and submitted an insurance claim for its losses.			

7.2 All audit working papers must be reviewed during the course of the audit.

The audit manager is reviewing the audit working papers on the current audit of Snodgrass Ltd. The audit is for the year ended 31 March 201X.She identifies a list of points made by audit staff and has to decide whether or not to investigate them further.

Based on the list of points below decide whether they should be investigated further.

✓

	Investigate	Do not investigate
(a) The company has decided to close its factory in South Wales after the year end with the loss of 120 jobs		
(b) On 1 March 201X company sold its buildings to Megabank plc, a finance company, and leased them back on a fifty year lease		
(c) The development project number 20R4 on which the company had spent £258,000 had been abandoned as unworkable as the proposed product could not be manufactured economically		
(d) The audit senior had queried whether it was correct that the sums receivable under a five year contract for the supply of component parts to a major customer has been taken into Revenues all in one year		
(e) The company has issued new shares on 2 April 201X		

7.3 You are reviewing the audit files following completion of the audit for three clients and find that the audit files contain the following points

For each client indicate whether or not you would recommend modifying the audit report and, if so, on what basis

Whoo Ltd

The auditors were appointed after the end of the financial year and discovered that the company had also changed banks shortly after the year end. The directors refused permission for the auditors to contact the previous bankers for confirmation of the year end bank balance without giving any good reason. The total of net current assets was £1.2m of which the bank balance amounted to £123,000 overdrawn.

		✓
(a)	Not modified	
Modified:		
(b)	'Except for' – limitation of audit scope	
(c)	'Except for' – material disagreement	
(d)	Disclaimer – pervasive limitation of audit scope	
(e)	Adverse opinion – pervasive disagreement	

Floo Ltd

The company had discovered a long term fraud perpetrated by the Financial Director. The amount stolen was believed to be of the order of £750,000. He had been prosecuted and jailed and action had commenced for recovery. The company was fully insured against fraud, so will not suffer any loss. However, the directors feel that the full story should be disclosed to the shareholders.

		✓
(a)	Not modified	
Modified:		
(b)	'Except for' limitation of audit scope	
(c)	'Except for' material disagreement	
(d)	Disclaimer – pervasive limitation of audit scope	
(e)	Adverse opinion – pervasive disagreement	

Bloo Ltd

The auditors have discovered that the company have invoiced several customers in full for services which they had agreed to supply over a period of two years. The whole of these amounts, totalling approximately £800,000 had been included in turnover. In addition Bloo has failed to make provision against two receivables balances amounting to £250,000 in total. The auditors have also indicated that inventories has been overvalued by approximately £300,000 as the directors have revalued old inventory to a current cost price. The pre tax profit of Bloo Limited is currently being shown at £3.1m and the net asset value at £12.5m.

The directors have made provision for their bonuses totalling £1.0m and are refusing to amend the financial statements for any of the points raised by the auditors.

		✓
(a)	Not modified	
Modified:		
(b)	'Except for' – limitation of audit scope	
(c)	'Except for' – material disagreement	
(d)	Disclaimer – pervasive limitation of audit scope	
(e)	Adverse opinion – pervasive disagreement	

7.4 The audit team at FluffyCo Ltd , a manufacturer of toys and games, have noted several points which they have brought to the attention of you, the audit partner. These include

- FluffyCo's product range has not changed in the last five years and newer products are appearing in the market which are in direct competition

- The management of FluffyCo have not replaced their Head of Marketing who has left the company to join a competitor

- The bank has refused to increase FluffyCo's overdraft and turned down an application for a loan for new equipment

- Orders from two key customers have declined steadily over the year and sales volumes are dropping. The directors point out that revenues are equivalent to those of the previous year but the auditors point out that this is due to price rises rather than the volume of goods sold

- The audit team reviewed the future budgets and cash flows of FluffyCo prepared by the directors and stated that, whilst some of the assumptions were optimistic the overall projections were not unreasonable

There are no other points which give any indication that the financial statements are incorrectly stated and the audit process was satisfactory.

You are to decide whether any of the above issues affect your audit opinion for the year. Indicate in the table below which course of action is the most appropriate in the circumstances.

	✓
(a) The company is likely to be in trouble so issue a qualified auditors' report on the financial statements on the basis that it is not a going concern	
(b) None of these points are of significance to the financial report for the current year and it is not for the auditors to tell the directors what to do so no action is required	
(c) None of these points is of significance to the financial report for the current financial year. However they indicate a worrying trend which it might be appropriate to discuss with the directors after the audit is finalised.	
(d) The audit team should go back to the company and try to discover further evidence that the company is not a going concern so that the audit report can be modified	

Answers to chapter activities

Chapter activities – answers
Introduction to auditing

1.1 (c) It enables them to carry out their audit without being influenced by their client

1.2 (b) The role of the auditor is to express an opinion to the shareholders on the truth and fairness of a set of financial statements

1.3 (a) True

(b) True

(c) False – reappoint by the shareholders

(d) False – only members of one of the Recognised Supervisory Bodies

1.4 (d) The members of the company

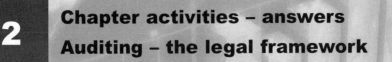

Chapter activities – answers

2 Auditing – the legal framework

2.1 (a) False – also to potential investors they are aware of

(b) True

(c) False – only liable collectively

2.2 All audit firms must have a system of **quality** control. This should include confirmation that **ethical** standards have been maintained, that the firm's **independence** from the client has not been compromised, that all audit work carried out has been reviewed and that the client continues to be acceptable. A **hot** review should take place where the audit is large or complex and a system of **cold** reviews implemented to ensure the firms audit procedures have been adhered to.

2.3 (a) True

(b) True

(c) False – only if it relates to their appointment

(d) True

(e) False

2.4

	Allowed	Not allowed
Auditors can include a disclaimer in their report to disclaim all liability for loss as the directors are responsible for the content		✓
Audit firms can operate as companies with limited liability	✓	
Audit firms can make agreements with individual shareholders and repay any losses they have incurred in the hope that not all shareholders will claim		✓
Auditors can include a disclaimer on their accounts to disclaim all liability for loss in respect of any third party apart from the shareholders		✓
Audit firms can agree a maximum amount of liability with the directors and shareholders of a client	✓	

3   Chapter activities – answers
Planning the audit assignment

3.1

Internal control:	Control activity/procedure:
Segregation of duties	Staff responsible for recording cash received are not responsible for processing sales invoices
Physical control	Limited access and password protection to the payroll system
Arithmetical and accounting checks	Matching of sales invoices to delivery notes and original sales order
Organisational controls	Supervisory responsibilities clearly defined
Authorisation controls	A requirement for two signatures on all company cheques

3.2

		Increase	Reduce	No effect
a)	The company exceeds its overdraft limit every month	✓		
b)	The company has introduced a bonus scheme for directors based on achieving revenue and profit targets	✓		
c)	The company has upgraded its payroll software		✓	
d)	Another firm of accountants has been approached to carry out internal audit reviews		✓	
e)	The audit manager has joined the company as financial director			✓

3.3

	Control objective	Risk	Control procedure
An aged receivables analysis is prepared monthly			✓
Invoices can be paid before goods are delivered		✓	
Goods are only purchased from approved suppliers	✓		
The payroll department is notified of starters and leavers by the personnel office			✓
The person responsible for collecting cash from vending machines pays the cash into the bank and notifies the cashiers department of the amount collected		✓	

3.4   (c) Payroll standard cost analysis

4

Chapter activities – answers
Audit testing

4.1

	Test of control	Substantive procedure
Carry out analytical review of payables (creditors) ledger balances		✓
Test a sample of purchase orders for authorisation	✓	
Reperform the bank reconciliation at year end		✓
Look for evidence that goods are despatched only to credit worthy customers	✓	
Check authorisation for new employees details added to payroll	✓	

4.2   (a), (b)and (d) are valid; (c) is not valid

4.3

	Current file	Permanent file
Audit points forward from prior years	✓	
Schedule of additions to fixed assets	✓	
Copy of the client's customer list		✓
Analytical comparison of results for previous five accounting periods	✓	
List of employees authorised to sign purchase orders and their authorisation limits		✓

4.4   (a) and (d) are TRUE; (b) and (c) are FALSE

5 Chapter activities – answers
Auditing accounting systems

5.1

Test	Assertion
Check sample of new employees details with personnel records	Existence
Check calculation of a sample of gross pay for hourly paid employees	Accuracy
Reconcile the wages control account	Classification

5.2

	Test data	Audit software
Stratification of ledger balances to provide data for sampling tests		✓
Input employee salary data to generate predicted payroll figures	✓	
Identify any gaps in the sequence of sales invoice number		✓

5.3   (b), (f) and (g) are STRENGTHS; (a), (d) and (e) are WEAKNESSES; (c) and (h) are NEITHER.

5.4

	Test of control	Substantive procedure
Check for evidence that supplier's accounts in the Payables Ledger are reconciled monthly to the statement from the supplier	✓	
Check for evidence that purchase invoices are batched before being input into the financial records and that batch details are recorded	✓	
Check that the numerical sequence of Goods Returned Notes is unbroken	✓	
Check that staff leaving employment are removed from the payroll promptly		✓
Physically inspect a sample of motor vehicles and record details		✓

6   Chapter activities – answers
Verification of assets and liabilities

6.1   (a), (b) and (c) are false; (d) is true.

6.2   (a), (d), (f), (g) and (h) are STRENGTHS; (b), (c), (e) and (i) are WEAKNESSES.

6.3   (c)   The provision against the contract in progress must be made (*to comply with SSAP 9*) and the property reclassified (*to comply with Companies Act 2006*) but no other adjustment need be made.

6.4   ■   Trade receivables has increased by % and revenue has increased by 15%
         Understated

         ■   Trade payables has increased by 9% and purchases has decreased by 12%
         Overstated

Chapter activities – answers
Audit completion and audit reporting

7

7.1   (a) and (e) – Amend financial statements; (c) and (d) – Ignore; (b) and (f) – Include in a note.

7.2   Investigate (b), (c) and (d); Do not investigate (a) and (e).

7.3   **Whoo Ltd**

(b)   'Except for' – limitation of audit scope

Floo Ltd

(a)   Not modified

Bloo Ltd

(e)   Adverse opinion – pervasive disagreement

7.4   (c)   None of these points is of significance to the financial report for the current financial year. However they indicate a worrying trend which it might be appropriate to discuss with the directors after the audit is finalised.

External auditing

Practice assessment 1

Please note, that in line with AAT sample material, this Assessment is divided into two parts, each with its own Task numbering system:

- External Auditing (Knowledge), on pages 34-41
- External Auditing (Skills), on pages 42-52

External Auditing (Knowledge)

Task 1.1

An audit benefits a company because it: ✓

(a)	Reassures the shareholders that the accounts are accurate	
(b)	Makes the management accountable to the shareholders	
(c)	Guarantees that the accounts are free from fraud or error	
(d)	Guarantees that the financial information shown is true and fair	

Choose one option.

Task 1.2

State whether the following statements are true or false.

	True	False
Auditors can limit their liability under a claim for negligence by agreement with the directors		
Audit firms are allowed to operate as limited liability companies		

Task 1.3

The role of the Auditing Practices Board does not include:

✓

(a)	establishing high standards of auditing	
(b)	meeting the developing needs of users of financial information	
(c)	ensuring public confidence in the auditing process	
(d)	issuing International Accounting Standards	

Choose one option.

Task 1.4

If the auditors assess the risk of a material misstatement as low, what would you expect the auditors to do? Choose one option.

✓

(a)	Not perform any substantive tests	
(b)	Perform a relatively small number of substantive tests	
(c)	Perform little or no compliance testing because control risks are assessed as low	
(d)	Adopt a risk based approach and limit the audit testing to a consideration of business risks	

Task 1.5

Which of the following statements best describes the auditors approach to materiality? Choose one option.

✓

(a)	The level of materiality is a matter for professional judgement	
(b)	Materiality is set at the planning stage and is not changed	
(c)	Materiality is based on the size of errors or misstatements the auditors will accept as reasonable	
(d)	Materiality limits are based on both the financial statements from previous years and the level of tolerable errors the auditors will accept in the current period	

Task 2.1

The external auditor may seek to place reliance on internal controls in order to restrict substantive testing.

In each of the following circumstances, select whether the external auditor is likely to place reliance on the internal control.

✓

	Reliance	No reliance
A company with an independent internal audit department		
A family company where the financial director is related to the chief executive		
A company where a fraud committed by the purchasing manager has been uncovered		

Task 2.2

Accounting systems have control objectives and control procedures to mitigate the risks that the control objective is not met.

For each of the following, select whether they are a control objective, risk, or control procedure.

✓

	Control objective	Risk	Control procedure
Organisations sell goods or services to customers with poor credit ratings			
Goods are purchased only from approved suppliers			
All purchase invoices must be matched to purchase orders and goods received notes			

Task 2.3

Segregation of duties is a fundamental principle of internal control.

It is established as a principle of internal control in order to ensure:

		✓
(a)	Employees cannot collude together to commit fraud	
(b)	No one person has complete control of any aspect of the accounting function	
(c)	No one individual can control the processing of a transaction from start to finish	
(d)	It is difficult to conceal errors or frauds	

Choose one option.

Task 3.1

As part of verification techniques in respect of revenues an auditor will inspect sales invoices. The auditor will gain assurance about different assertions depending on the information on the invoice.

In respect of the information below, select the assertion for which that information will provide assurance.

✓

	Accuracy	Classification	Cut-off	Existence
Date of the invoice				
Description of the item sold				
Monetary amount				

Task 3.2

Auditors use samples in their audit testing. In which of the following situations is the use of sampling not appropriate:

✓

(a) When the population is homogenous	
(b) When all items in the population have an equal chance of being selected	
(c) When the population is very small and all the items are material	
(d) When the population consists of a large number of transactions	

Task 3.3

Auditors use tests of control and substantive procedures to gather audit evidence.

For each of the procedures listed below, select whether it is a test of control or a substantive procedure.

✓

	Test of control	Substantive procedure
Reperformance of the bank reconciliation at the date of the statement of financial position		
Comparison of the current year's results with last year and with the budget for the current year		
Check for authorisation of overtime payments		

Task 3.4

Two types of computer-assisted audit techniques (CAAT) are test data and audit software.

For each of the procedures listed below, select the type of CAAT which would be used to perform that procedure.

✓

	Test data	Audit software
Select all sales ledger accounts showing a credit balance for review		
Input of inventory (stock) issues in excess of balance of inventory items shown on inventory records		
Select all accounts in the receivables (sales) ledger where balance exceeds credit limit		

Task 3.5

An external auditor is required to obtain an understanding of the control environment within an audited entity.

Select whether the following factors contribute to a strong control environment, a weak control environment, or have no effect.

✓

	Strong	Weak	No effect
The organisation has an internal audit department which reports to the Financial Director			
Management takes the view that office staff are costly so keeps staff levels in the accounts department to a minimum			
The Financial Director is a qualified accountant who has been with the company for twenty years and was previously the financial controller			
The external auditors carry out extensive substantive testing of balances in the Statement of Financial Position (Balance Sheet)			

Task 4.1

External auditors use a variety of methods for documenting systems of control, including flowcharts, internal control questionnaires, and internal control checklists.

You are the audit manager documenting a client's financial systems. Which is the most appropriate way of documenting a client's financial systems in the following situations, using a flowchart, narrative notes or an internal control questionnaire (ICQ)?

✓

	Flowchart	Narrative notes	ICQ
Creating a representation of the purchases system to indicate internal controls			
Making enquiries of staff as to day-to-day operations			
Identifying possible areas for fraud within the payroll system			

Task 4.2

Select whether the following statements in respect of an external auditor's working papers are true or false.

✓

	True	False
The auditor must be able to show they have gathered evidence to substantiate their audit opinion		
All audit working papers should show evidence of review		
The Permanent File contains the audit programme and all the background data for the client		

External Auditing (Skills)

Task 1.1

Greenhouse runs gardening maintenance services on a contract basis. All gardeners are self employed and are sent to each location by Greenhouse. Greenhouse is responsible for advertising its services in local newspapers and pays for any advertising at the time it is placed. It employs three people who take calls from customers and allocate work to the gardeners.

Each gardener pays Greenhouse a monthly fee to be registered with them. Each gardener negotiates a price with the customer and collects their fee directly from the customer after the work has been completed. Gardeners supply their own tools and materials.

Which one of the following combinations of accounting systems is likely to be subject to external audit?

✓

(a) Revenues, Trade Receivables and Trade Payables	
(b) Purchases, Trade Payables	
(c) Revenues, Purchases and Payroll	
(d) Purchases, Trade Receivables and Trade Payables	

Task 1.2

The external auditor assesses control risk in order to determine the audit approach.

Select whether the following factors are likely to lead to the auditor assessing that there is an increase or decrease in control risk.

✓

	Increase	Decrease
A new company accountant has been appointed who is unqualified		
The management has decided to cut costs and has made two people redundant from the accounts department		
New computerised accounting systems have been installed but the staff training programme has not been completed		

Task 1.3

An entity uses internal control procedures in order to mitigate the risks to which the entity is exposed. Listed below are two internal control procedures which are applicable to an entity's sales and receivables system.

From the list below select which risk is mitigated by each internal control procedure:

■ Sales are made to customers who cannot pay

■ Sales are not made to existing customers

■ Deliveries are not made to bona fide customers

■ Customer refuses to pay for goods allegedly not received

■ Customer orders not being fulfilled

Internal control procedure	Risk mitigated
Customers' outstanding balances are checked against their credit limits before sales orders are accepted	
Goods delivered to customers are accompanied by two copies of the Delivery Note. One is signed by the customer and is retained in the Despatch Department the other is retained by the customer	

Task 1.4

The following are descriptions of procedures within the sales system of Bugle Ltd.

For each procedure, select whether it is a strength or a weakness.

✓

	Strength	Weakness
Sales invoices are processed by James who also banks the monies received from customers		
The sales order department telephones customer orders through to the despatch department which then delivers the goods to customers together with a delivery note		
Customers are not sent a monthly statement. James is responsible for collecting overdue debts and issuing credit notes where necessary		

Task 1.5

The figures below are a summary of an analytical review of the draft financial statements of Howdo Ltd. The review was carried out at the planning stage and the comparison was made against the original budget for the financial year.

Based on the results of this review indicate whether or not you would investigate or accept the reason for any differences

✓

		Actual	Budget	Investigate	Accept
(a)	Gross profit	56%	64%		
(b)	Net profit margin	12%	14%		
(c)	Receivables days	38 days	42 days		
(d)	Payables days	36 days	49 days		
(e)	Inventory turnover	9 times	12 times		

Task 1.6

The objective of a substantive test will determine the population from which the sample for testing is selected.

For each of the objectives set out below, select the population from which the sample should be selected.

(a) Obtain evidence of the existence of inventories

> **Inventory records / Inventory count**

(b) Obtain evidence that the organisation only purchases the goods it needs

> **Purchase orders / Purchase invoices**

Task 1.7

The audit work to be carried out requires the verification of cut-off procedures to ensure that all transactions are recorded in the correct accounting period.

During the year end inventory count on 31 March 201X the audit team recorded the following transactions.

The last Goods Received Note number was 10672.

Which invoices should be recorded in purchases for the year? Select one option from the second table below.

Invoice no. ref	Supplier	Invoice date	GRN number	Amount
95493	Big Trumpet plc	28 March	10674	£3,098.45
95494	Last Post Ltd	31 March	10671	£12,274.20
94495	Bugle Ltd	29 March	10673	£1,567.90
94496	Bangalong Ltd	30 March	10672	£12,786.42
94497	Simbol plc	1 April	10670	£456.48
94498	Twangalong Ltd	31 March	10675	£998.46

	✓
(a)　All of them except 94497 as this is dated after the year end	
(b)　95494, 94496 and 94497	
(c)　95493, 95494 and 94496	
(d)　95493, 95494, 94495 and 94496	

Task 1.8

You are auditing Megabuild plc a company which carries out large projects, mostly overseas. At present Megabuild is building a dam in the Philippines, a motorway in South Africa and a holiday village in Egypt.

The audit team has been asked to devise audit procedures for the verification of work in progress balances as part of inventories. From the list of procedures below state whether you would include them as valid or exclude them as invalid tests.

✓

Procedures	Valid	Invalid
(a) Read contracts and note estimated completion date and penalty clauses		
(b) Visit each construction site to verify stage of completion of the contract		
(c) Review costing system and allocation of costs to each contract		
(d) Review calculation of profit to be taken on all contracts at least 50% completed		
(e) Review basis of allocation of overheads to contract and check sample of calculations		

Task 2.1

The errors listed below have been detected during the audit of BiggBatt Ltd. The directors of BiggBatt refuse to make adjustments to correct the errors.

The audit firm Tickett & Wrunne set a performance materiality level of 5% of profit before tax as the yardstick to determine whether errors are material. BiggBatt Ltd's profit before tax is £250,000.

Select whether or not the following errors need to be adjusted in order that Tickett & Wrunne can issue an unmodified audit opinion on the financial statements.

(Note – examples are individual, not cumulative)

✓

	Requires to be adjusted	Does not require to be adjusted
An overstatement of receivables (debtors) amounting to £7,000, and an understatement of payables (creditors) amounting to £4,800		
Incorrect depreciation calculations amounting to £9,000 understated and an overstatement of inventory (stock) values amounting to £6,400		
Understatement of director's bonuses amounting to £10,000		

Task 2.2

Jellybean Ltd is a manufacturer of sweets and confectionery. It purchases raw materials, sugar, colouring, syrups, flavour enhancers etc in bulk quantities. Sweets and confectionery is sold in boxes and bags. Jellybean sells under its own 'Suckitandsee' range and also makes confectionery and sweets for other retailers which are sold under their own brand names.

You are to set out, in a manner suitable for inclusion in the audit plan, the audit procedures to be undertaken in order to ensure that raw material and finished goods inventories are fairly stated in the financial statements.

Task 2.3

You are an audit senior on the audit of Bongo plc. During the course of the audit you discover that the purchasing manager has an interest in a company which is one of Bongo Ltd's major suppliers. You ask the manager about this. He states that the interest is actually not his but his wife's and that the Purchasing Director is aware of the situation and has no objection to it. All transactions are at arms length and the company does not appear to receive any preferential terms.

In respect of this matter, select whether the audit senior should take no further action or refer to the audit manager.

No further action / Refer to audit manager

Task 2.4

During the external audit of Acorn Ltd, the audit junior identified several instances where overtime payments were not authorised by the factory manager. Investigations revealed that these were at times when the manager was away on holiday or meeting suppliers and was not available to sign. In all other instances overtime was properly authorised.

In respect of this matter, select whether the audit junior should take no further action or refer to the audit supervisor.

No further action / Refer to audit supervisor

Task 3.1

During the course of the audit of the purchasing system at Whoppa Ltd, a manufacturer of double glazed windows and doors, the audit team identifies that there are no procedures for approving suppliers and that purchase orders are always sent to the same few suppliers.

Whoppa has used the same suppliers for many years and the team is told that they have a good relationship with them. The team is told that these are regular suppliers who know what Whoppa's requirements are, they are reliable and provide goods of the right quality. The purchasing assistant thinks that approving suppliers is a waste of time and that they would end up selecting the same suppliers anyway so does not see the point of doing it.

Prepare extracts, suitable for inclusion in a report to management of Whoppa Ltd, which set out

(i)   the possible consequences of these two problem areas and

(ii)   the recommendations that you would make in respect of this matter.

It is suggested that you set out your answer in the form of a table, as follows:

Problem areas	Consequences	Recommendation
no procedures for approving suppliers		
purchase orders always sent to the same few suppliers		

Task 3.2

You are reviewing the files following completion of the audit work on three audit clients and find that the audit files contain the following points.

In each instance indicate how the problems identified might affect the Auditors' Report.

Bing Ltd

The audit team was unable to physically inspect vehicles and equipment to the value of £3.2m as part of tangible assets with a value of £5m as they were situated in various locations throughout the country. The audit team were unable to check whether individual items were insured as no details of individual assets were given. Vehicle log books were inspected for all vehicles. Purchase invoices had been seen for all additions and sales invoices for all disposals. The asset register was reconciled to the nominal ledger.

		✓
(a)	Not modified	
	Modified:	
(b)	'Except for' – limitation of scope	
(c)	'Except for' – material disagreement	
(d)	Disclaimer – pervasive limitation of scope	
(e)	Adverse opinion – pervasive disagreement	

Bong Ltd

You are auditing the annual accounts which have been prepared in the same way as those of previous periods. You discover that the company had recently defaulted on the payment of a quarterly loan instalment which was due one month after the year end. They attributed this to a 'financing error' and made the required repayment two weeks later than they should have done. You discover that to make the payment the company had taken out a short term loan from another company owned by the Managing Director's brother. The company had been at the limit of its overdraft facilities throughout the financial period. The repayment of the loan to the Managing Director's brother together with another quarterly loan repayment is due in two months. You discover that the bank has written to the company stating that if the repayment was late this time they would be demanding the repayment of the whole loan amount immediately. If this happens, it is obvious that the company could not meet this demand.

		✓
(a)	Not modified	
	Modified:	
(b)	'Except for' – limitation of scope	
(c)	'Except for' – material disagreement	
(d)	Disclaimer – pervasive limitation of scope	
(e)	Adverse opinion – pervasive disagreement	

continued

Bang Ltd

You have been appointed auditors three months after the year-end as Bang Ltd's previous audit firm resigned. The company is a manufacturer and distributor of electrical components. It has a very efficient internal audit department and your systems audit work reveals no major weaknesses except for some internal control weaknesses in the purchasing system, none of which are of major significance. You carry out substantive testing on items in the Statement of Financial Position and these, again, give no cause for concern except you are unable to verify the existence of some of the non-current assets as they were sold after the year end.

	✓
(a) Not modified	
Modified:	
(b) 'Except for' – limitation of scope	
(c) 'Except for' – material disagreement	
(d) Disclaimer – pervasive limitation of scope	
(e) Adverse opinion – pervasive disagreement	

Task 3.3

During the course of the audit of Mungo Ltd, a construction company, you discover that the company may be paying bribes in order to obtain work. Your evidence is based on various unexplained 'round sum' cash payments which have been included as 'site costs' in the nominal ledger. Some of these payments amount to several thousand pounds and there does not appear to be any documentation to support the amounts paid. There does not appear to be any commercial reason why such substantial cash payments are being made. When you questioned the management and staff you were told that the Sales Director was responsible and had all the paperwork as these items were confidential. The Sales Director is proving very elusive and constantly avoids you.

Should you . . .   ✓

(a) Do nothing, except continue to pursue the Sales Director, because to go any further would breach your duty of confidentiality to your client?	
(b) Report the matter to the Police anonymously?	
(c) Contact the customer and report the matter as being possible bribery of their employees?	
(d) Contact the press and reveal the whole story publicly?	

Choose one option.

External auditing

Practice assessment 2

This Assessment is based on a sample assessment provided by the AAT and is reproduced here with their kind permission.

Please note that this Assessment is divided into two parts, each with its own Task numbering system:

- External Auditing (Knowledge), on pages 54-60
- External Auditing (Skills), on pages 61-70

External Auditing (Knowledge)

Task 1.1

Complete the statement below on the overall objectives of the external auditor in conducting an audit of financial statements by filling in the gaps with terms from the following selection:

- Absolute
- All
- An applicable financial framework
- Express an opinion
- International Standards on Auditing
- Material
- Provide a guarantee
- Reasonable

The overall objectives of the external auditor are to obtain . . . . assurance

about whether the financial statements are free from . . . . misstatement, whether

due to fraud or error, thereby enabling the auditor to . . . . on whether the financial

statements are prepared in all material respects in accordance with . . . .

Task 1.2

State whether the following statements are true or false in respect of external auditors' liability.

	True	False
External auditors are liable to anybody who relies solely on the audit report on financial statements when making investment decisions		
External auditors may limit their liability to third parties if they include a disclaimer of liability in their audit report		

Task 1.3

Which one of the following best describes the role of the International Auditing and Assurance Board (IAASB)?

The IAASB is responsible for: ✓

(a) Setting auditing standards which are compulsory throughout the world	
(b) Monitoring auditors to ensure that they comply with auditing standards	
(c) Investigating and disciplining auditors who fail to comply with auditing standards	
(d) Setting auditing standards which facilitate the convergence of national and international auditing standards	

Task 1.4

When planning an audit of financial statements, the external auditor is required to consider how factors such as the entity's operating environment and its system of internal control affect the risk of misstatement in the financial statements.

Select whether the following factors are likely to increase, reduce, or have no effect on the risk of misstatement.

✓

	Increase	Reduce	No effect
The entity is committed to employing personnel with appropriate accounting and financial reporting skills			
The entity is to be sold and the purchase consideration will be determined as a multiple of reported profit			
The entity's management does not intend to remedy deficiencies in internal controls identified by the external auditor			

Task 1.5

Select whether the following statements in respect of performance materiality are true or false.

	True	False
Performance materiality should be set at a level below the level of materiality for the financial statements as a whole		
Once established, performance materiality must not be changed as the audit progresses		

Task 2.1

The external auditor may seek to place reliance on internal controls in order to restrict substantive testing.

In each of the following circumstances, select whether the external auditor is likely to place reliance or place no reliance on internal controls.

	Reliance	No reliance
A company where the processing of accounting transactions is undertaken by one person		
A company which has an internal audit function which monitors operational and financial controls		
A company which has internal controls with a history of management override		

Task 2.2

Accounting systems have control objectives and control procedures to mitigate the risks that the control objective is not met.

For each of the following, select whether they are a control objective, risk, or control procedure.

✓

	Control objective	Risk	Control procedure
Customers fail to pay for goods received			
All goods leaving the warehouse are invoiced			
Sequence check on despatch/delivery note numbers			

Task 2.3

Complete the below definition of internal controls by filling in the gaps with terms from the following list:

■ Absolute

■ Accounting and reporting standards

■ Accounting records

■ Financial reporting

■ Laws and regulations

■ Reasonable

The process designed, implemented and maintained by those charged with governance,

management and other personnel, to provide . . . . assurance about the achievement

of an entity's objectives with regard to the reliability of . . . ., effectiveness and

efficiency of operations and compliance with applicable . . . .

Task 3.1

As part of verification techniques in respect of purchases, an auditor will inspect purchase invoices. The auditor will gain assurance about different assertions depending on the information on the invoice.

In respect of the information below, select the assertion for which that information will provide assurance.

	Accuracy	Classification	Cut-off	Existence
Date of the invoice				
Description of the item purchased				
Monetary amount				

Task 3.2

When selecting items in order to perform tests of detail, the auditor has to consider a number of factors.

For each of the following factors, select whether they will result in an increase or a decrease in sample size.

	Increase	Decrease
An increase in the auditor's assessment of risk of misstatement		
An increase in the use of other substantive procedures directed at the same assertion		
Stratification of the population being tested		

Task 3.3

Auditors use tests of control and substantive procedures to gather audit evidence.

For each of the procedures listed below, select whether it is a test of control or a substantive procedure.

✓

	Test of control	Substantive procedure
Comparison of the current year's revenue figure with the previous year's figure		
Observation of the despatch procedures in respect of goods leaving an entity's warehouse		
Vouching of an addition to non-current assets to the supplier's invoice		

Task 3.4

Two types of computer-assisted audit techniques (CAAT) are test data and audit software.

For each of the procedures listed below, select the type of CAAT which would be used to perform that procedure.

✓

	Test data	Audit software
Comparison of the cost and net realisable value of inventory items to determine the lower value		
Input of data with false inventory code numbers to check that the system rejects such data		
Extraction of inventory balances over £5,000 in order to carry out further testing		

Task 3.5

An external auditor is required to obtain an understanding of the control environment within an audited entity.

Select whether the following factors contribute to a strong control environment, a weak control environment, or have no effect.

✓

	Strong	Weak	No effect
Management is competent and acts with integrity			
Management has not made an assessment of the risk of fraud			

Task 4.1

External auditors use a variety of methods for documenting systems of control, including flowcharts, internal control questionnaires, and internal control checklists.

For each of the following descriptions select whether it represents a flowchart, internal control questionnaire, or internal control checklist.

✓

	Flowchart	Questionnaire	Checklist
A listing of controls necessary to provide reasonable assurance of effective internal control within a given transaction cycle			
A pictorial presentation of the processing steps within a given transaction cycle			

Task 4.2

Select whether the following statements in respect of an external auditor's working papers are true or false.

✓

	True	False
Working papers are prepared by the external auditor because there is a legal requirement to do so		
The objective of working papers is to provide evidence that the audit was planned and performed in accordance with International Standards on Auditing		
Working papers should contain the name of who performed the audit work and the date it was performed		

External Auditing (Skills)

Task 1.1

Cleanco Ltd is a company which undertakes commercial and domestic cleaning work. The company provides labour and cleaning materials. All purchases of cleaning materials are paid for at time of purchase and Cleanco Ltd's employees collect the fee as soon as each job is completed.

In addition to cash handling activities, which one of the following combinations of accounting systems is likely to be subject to external audit?

		✓
(a)	Sales, trade receivables and trade payables	
(b)	Purchases, trade payables and payroll	
(c)	Sales, purchases and payroll	
(d)	Purchases, trade receivables and trade payables	

Task 1.2

The external auditor assesses control risk in order to determine the audit approach.

Select whether the following factors are likely to lead to the auditor assessing that there is an increase or decrease in control risk.

	Increase	Decrease
The allocation of responsibilities so that different personnel are responsible for the authorisation, processing and recording of transactions		
Management has a positive attitude and discipline towards controls and their enforcement		
The accounting staff are inexperienced and have a poor understanding of accounting principles		

Task 1.3

An entity uses internal control procedures in order to mitigate (reduce the level of) the risks to which the entity is exposed. Listed below are two internal control procedures which are applicable to an entity's inventory procurement system.

Match each internal control procedure with the risk mitigated from the list below:

- ▪ Purchasing goods from unauthorised suppliers
- ▪ Theft of inventory
- ▪ Purchasing unnecessary goods
- ▪ Paying for goods not received

Internal control procedure	Risk mitigated
Purchase invoices matched to goods received records prior to posting to the ledger	
Physical counts of inventory and reconciliation with recorded amounts	

Task 1.4

The following are descriptions of procedures within the payroll system of Delaware Ltd.

For each procedure, select whether it is a strength or a weakness.

✓

	Strength	Weakness
The computerised payroll is processed weekly by Amelia who is also responsible for amending the standing data details such as the addition of new employees and changes to wage rates.		
The managing director, David Delaware, reviews the BACS listing of net pay details per employee and signs the listing before authorising the assistant accountant, Marie, to transmit the details to the company's bank.		

Task 1.5

The external auditor is required to undertake analytical procedures as part of the planning process in order to identify the risk of misstatement of figures in the financial statements. The results of the analytical procedures conducted on trade receivables and trade payables in the financial statements of an audit client are listed below.

Select whether the results indicate that trade receivables and trade payables might have been under or overstated.

	Understated	*Overstated*
Trade receivables have increased by 20% and revenue have increased by 5%		
Trade payables have decreased by 10% and purchases have decreased by 7%		

Task 1.6

The objective of a substantive test will determine the population from which the sample for testing is selected.

For each of the objectives set out below, select the population from which the sample should be selected.

(a) Obtain evidence of the existence of a non-current asset

Non-current asset register / Physical asset

(b) Obtain evidence of the completeness of the trade payables balance

Purchase ledger entries / Goods received records

Task 1.7

An audit junior performed direct confirmations on a sample of trade receivables balances of Oak Ltd at 31 March 20X9, and has reconciled the balance on one customer's reply to Oak Ltd's sales ledger balance as follows:

	£
Balance outstanding per customer's reply	25,200
(i) Payment 31 March 20X9 by cheque per customer's records not on Oak Ltd's ledger	8,300
(ii) Sales invoice 27 March 20X9 not accepted by customer as goods were returned	5,400
Balance outstanding per Oak Ltd's sales ledger	38,900

The audit junior has asked for guidance on the further work to be performed in respect of this reconciliation.

Using two of the following terms, complete the statements below to indicate which of Oak Ltd's accounting records each of the reconciling items should be checked to.

- ■   Pre year-end bank statement
- ■   Post year-end bank statement
- ■   Goods despatch note
- ■   Goods returned note

(i)   Payment 31 March 20X9 by cheque should be checked to. . . . .

(ii) Sales invoice 27 March 20X9 not accepted should be checked to. . . . .

Task 1.8

During the year ended 31 December 20X9, Becks Ltd took out a bank loan of £1 million to fund a capital project. The terms of the loan require:

■ Capital repayments, over 5 years, in monthly instalments commencing 1 July 20X9

■ Interest at 9% per annum payable monthly

■ Profit before interest and tax in the monthly management accounts to cover interest at least four times

Set out, in a manner suitable for inclusion in the audit plan:

(i) The audit risks relating to the loan; and

(ii) The procedures to be undertaken in order to ensure that the loan is properly classified and disclosed in the financial statements.

Task 2.1

The error listed below has been detected during the audit of Taurus Ltd. The directors of Taurus refuse to make an adjustment to correct the error.

The audit firm Able Kahn LLP uses 5% of profit before tax as the yardstick to determine whether errors are material. Taurus Ltd's profit before tax is £100,000.

Select whether or not the following error requires to be adjusted in order to issue an unmodified audit opinion on the financial statements.

An overstatement of inventory amounting to £4,200, and an overstatement of receivables amounting to £3,800

> **Requires to be adjusted / Does not require to be adjusted**

Task 2.2

Engco Ltd is a company which undertakes industrial maintenance services under short-term fixed-price contracts. All direct costs (labour and materials) relating to each contract are recorded in the company's job costing system which is integrated with the purchases and payroll applications. The job costing records are used by the finance director to estimate the value of work in progress for the monthly management accounts and the year-end financial statements. For the work in progress valuation, a percentage is added to the direct costs to cover overheads. The finance director determines the percentage by taking the production overheads figure in the management accounts as a percentage of direct costs in the management accounts.

Set out, in a manner suitable for inclusion in the audit plan, the audit procedures to be undertaken in order to ensure that work in progress is fairly stated in the financial statements.

Task 2.3

During the external audit of Beech Ltd, the audit junior identified an invoice for the cost of school fees for the managing director's children. The purchase ledger clerk informed the audit junior that the managing director had told her to hide the costs in sundries. The amount of the school fees is insignificant in terms of key figures in the financial statements.

In respect of this matter, select whether the audit junior should take no further action or refer to the supervisor.

No further action / Refer to supervisor

Task 2.4

During the external audit of Pike Ltd, the audit junior identified two instances of failure to authorise purchase invoices prior to posting to the purchase ledger. Both instances occurred when the purchase supervisor who is responsible for authorising such transactions was away on sick leave, and further tests indicated no similar failings following her return to work.

In respect of this matter, select whether the audit junior should take no further action or refer to the supervisor.

No further action / Refer to supervisor

Task 3.1

During the audit of Media Ltd, a film production company, it was discovered that although the company maintained a non-current asset register to record the details of its cameras and other equipment, no checking procedures other than reconciliation with the nominal ledger are undertaken.

Prepare extracts, suitable for inclusion in a report to management of Media Ltd, which set out

(i)   the possible consequences of this

(ii)   the recommendations that you would make

in respect of this matter.

Task 3.2

For each of the following situations which have arisen in dealings with two unrelated audit clients, select whether or not the audit opinion on the financial statements would be modified.

(a) Alpha Ltd capitalised costs of £150,000 in respect of repairs and maintenance and included these costs in non-current assets. The amount capitalised represents 30% of Alpha Ltd's profit before tax. The directors refuse to make any adjustments in respect of this matter.

Modified / Not modified

(b) There is a significant uncertainty about Beta Ltd's ability to continue as a going concern. The directors of Beta Ltd have prepared the financial statements on a going concern basis and have fully disclosed the uncertainty in the notes to the financial statements.

Modified / Not modified

Task 3.3

During the audit of Medlar Ltd, the audit senior discovered that the managing director Peter Nash regularly pockets cash received from customers and does not include any details relating to the transaction in the accounting records of the business. Furthermore, none of this cash has been included as income on Peter Nash's tax return.

Which one of the following is the appropriate action for the audit senior to take?

Report the matter to:

		✓
(a)	The tax authorities after discussion with Peter Nash	
(b)	The tax authorities without discussion with Peter Nash	
(c)	Your firm's money laundering reporting officer after discussion with Peter Nash	
(d)	Your firm's money laundering reporting officer without discussion with Peter Nash	

Practice assessment 1
– answers

External Auditing (Knowledge)

Task 1.1

(b)   Makes the management accountable to the shareholders

Task 1.2

Auditors can limit their liability under a claim for negligence by agreement with the directors (**false** – only by agreement with the shareholders)

Audit firms are allowed to operate as limited liability companies   (**true**)

Task 1.3

(d)   issuing International Accounting Standards (this is carried out by the IAASB)

Task 1.4

(b)   Perform a relatively small number of substantive tests

Task 1.5

(a)   The level of materiality is a matter for professional judgement

Task 2.1

	Reliance	No reliance
A company with an independent internal audit department	✓	
A family company where the financial director is related to the chief executive		✓
A company where a fraud committed by the purchasing manager has been uncovered		✓

Task 2.2

	Control objective	Risk	Control procedure
Organisations sell goods or services to customers with poor credit ratings		✓	
Goods are purchased only from approved suppliers	✓		
All purchase invoices must be matched to purchase orders and goods received notes			✓

Task 2.3

(c)   No one individual can control the processing of a transaction from start to finish

Task 3.1

	Accuracy	Classification	Cut-off	Existence
Date of the invoice			✓	
Description of the item sold		✓		
Monetary amount	✓			

Task 3.2

(c)   When the population is very small and all the items are material

Task 3.3

	Test of control	Substantive procedure
Reperformance of the bank reconciliation at the date of the statement of financial position		✓
Comparison of the current year's results with last year and with the budget for the current year		✓
Check for authorisation of overtime payments	✓	

Task 3.4

	Test data	Audit software
Select all sales ledger accounts showing a credit balance for review		✓
Input of inventory (stock) issues in excess of balance of inventory items shown on inventory records	✓	
Select all accounts in the receivables (sales) ledger where balance exceeds credit limit		✓

Task 3.5

	Strong	Weak	No effect
The organisation has an internal audit department which reports to the Financial Director		✓	
Management takes the view that office staff are costly so keeps staff levels in the accounts department to a minimum		✓	
The Financial Director is a qualified accountant who has been with the company for twenty years and was previously the financial controller	✓		
The external auditors carry out extensive substantive testing of balances in the Statement of Financial Position (Balance Sheet)			✓

Task 4.1

	Flowchart	Narrative notes	ICQ
Creating a representation of the purchases system to indicate internal controls	✓		
Making enquiries of staff as to day-to-day operations			✓
Identifying possible areas for fraud within the payroll system	✓		

Task 4.2

	True	False
The auditor must be able to show they have gathered evidence to substantiate their audit opinion	✓	
All audit working papers should show evidence of review	✓	
The Permanent File contains the audit programme and all the background data for the client		✓

External Auditing (Skills)

Task 1.1

(c)   Revenues, Purchases and Payroll

Task 1.2

There is an **increase** in control risk in ALL cases.

Task 1.3

Internal control procedure	Risk mitigated
Customers' outstanding balances are checked against their credit limits before sales orders are accepted	Sales are made to customers who cannot pay
Goods delivered to customers are accompanied by two copies of the Delivery Note. One is signed by the customer and is retained in the Despatch Department the other is retained by the customer	Customer refuses to pay for goods allegedly not received

Task 1.4

ALL procedures would be considered a **weakness**.

Task 1.5

		Actual	Budget	Investigate	Accept
(a)	Gross profit	56%	64%	✓	
(b)	Net profit margin	12%	14%		✓
(c)	Receivables days	38 days	42 days		✓
(d)	Payables days	36 days	49 days	✓	
(e)	Inventory turnover	9 times	12 times	✓	

Task 1.6

(a)   **Inventory count**

(b)   **Purchase orders**

Task 1.7

(b)   95494, 94496 and 94497

Task 1.8

	Procedure	Valid	Invalid
(a)	Read contracts and note estimated completion date and penalty clauses	✓	
(b)	Visit each construction site to verify stage of completion of the contract		✓
(c)	Review costing system and allocation of costs to each contract	✓	
(d)	Review calculation of profit to be taken on all contracts at least 50% completed	✓	
(e)	Review basis of allocation of overheads to contract and check sample of calculations	✓	

Task 2.1

	Requires to be adjusted	Does not require to be adjusted
An overstatement of receivables (debtors) amounting to £7,000, and an understatement of payables (creditors) amounting to £4,800		✓
Incorrect depreciation calculations amounting to £9,000 understated and an overstatement of inventory (stock) values amounting to £6,400	✓	
Understatement of director's bonuses amounting to £10,000	✓	

Task 2.2

Answer should include some or all of the following:

Attend the client's inventory count and:

■   observe the client's staff carrying out the count in accordance with their instructions

■   note any deviation from inventory count instructions for later discussion with the client's management

■   select a sample of items and count them independently for comparison with the client's count

■   ensure that all items checked are detailed on audit working papers, together with any observed problems with the count

■   if any tests prove unsatisfactory, request a recount be performed by the auditors and client staff

■   where boxed goods are stored in stacks, ensure the stacks are complete and not hollow

■   ask the client's staff to open a sample number of boxes to ensure the contents are as stated on the label

■   note any damaged, obsolete or slow-moving inventory to ensure that these are separately identified and can be appropriately valued

■   make a note of the count sheet numbers to ensure that all sheets are accounted for

■   select a sample of the client's completed inventory count sheets and take a copy for comparison with the final versions used for inventory valuation

■   note details of the last delivery of items into inventory and the last issue from inventory – details of the last delivery note or goods received note number should be recorded

Check valuation of inventory:

■   check sample of costs with original purchase documentation eg invoices

■   review sales after year end to ensure goods not sold under value

■   in addition to arithmetical tests such as those detailed above, auditors should also use analytical review to test the valuation of inventory

Check cut off

■   review purchase invoices entered in to the company records shortly before and after the year end and match them to the GRN to ensure that they are recorded in the correct accounting period

■   review GRNs after the year end and ensure that none of these have been included in inventory or payables for the current financial period

■   check records of goods returned to suppliers before the year end to ensure that any credit notes due have either been received or accrued

■   check sales invoices before and after the year end to ensure that goods despatched to customers have been invoiced in the correct accounting period

Task 2.3

Refer to audit manager

Task 2.4

No further action

Task 3.1	Consequences	Recommendations
The company does not have any procedure for approving suppliers	Suppliers may not be the most competitive for quality and service Suppliers may become financially unsound Dependence on a limited number of suppliers may put the continuity of supplies at risk	The performance of all suppliers to the company should be reviewed periodically All suppliers capable of delivering product reliably at the right price and quality should be invited to tender for a supply contract All suppliers given a supply contract should be required to demonstrate their ability to continue to trade for the period of the contract
Purchase orders are always sent to the same few suppliers	The company may not be obtaining the best prices Suppliers may become complacent and the quality of service may decline Relationships may develop between suppliers and staff who order goods. This may lead to staff becoming too friendly with suppliers and not challenging prices or quality, or suppliers bribing staff to maintain the flow of orders	Individual members of staff should be rotated so they do not build up cosy relationships with suppliers Performance of suppliers should be monitored. Poor service should be challenged Suppliers' prices should be compared with other suppliers' prices regularly to ensure that the company continues to buy goods at the best price

Task 3.2

Bing Ltd   (a)   Not modified

Bong Ltd   (e)   Adverse opinion – pervasive disagreement (Going concern)

Bang Ltd   (b)   'Except for' limitation of scope (unable to attend inventory count. Unable to verify existence of assets)

Task 3.3

(a)   Do nothing, except continue to pursue the Sales Director, as to go any further would breach your duty of confidentiality to your client

(You have no evidence that bribes are actually being paid. Until you can clarify the situation with the Sales Director you cannot breach client confidentiality)

Practice assessment 2 – answers

External Auditing (Knowledge)

Task 1.1

The overall objectives of the external auditor are to obtain **reasonable** assurance about whether the financial statements are free from **material** misstatement, whether due to fraud or error, thereby enabling the auditor to **express an opinion** on whether the financial statements are prepared in all material respects in accordance with **an applicable financial framework**.

Task 1.2

	True	False
External auditors are liable to anybody who relies solely on the audit report on financial statements when making investment decisions		✓
External auditors may limit their liability to third parties if they include a disclaimer of liability in their audit report	✓	

Task 1.3

The IAASB is responsible for: **(d)** Setting auditing standards which facilitate the convergence of national and international auditing standards

Task 1.4

	Increase	Reduce	No effect
The entity is committed to employing personnel with appropriate accounting and financial reporting skills		✓	
The entity is to be sold and the purchase consideration will be determined as a multiple of reported profit	✓		
The entity's management does not intend to remedy deficiencies in internal controls identified by the external auditor	✓		

Task 1.5

	True	False
Performance materiality should be set at a level below the level of materiality for the financial statements as a whole	✓	
Once established, performance materiality must not be changed as the audit progresses		✓

Task 2.1

	Reliance	No reliance
A company where the processing of accounting transactions is undertaken by one person		✓
A company which has an internal audit function which monitors operational and financial controls	✓	
A company which has internal controls with a history of management override		✓

Task 2.2

	Control objective	Risk	Control procedure
Customers fail to pay for goods received		✓	
All goods leaving the warehouse are invoiced	✓		
Sequence check on despatch/delivery note numbers			✓

Task 2.3

The process designed, implemented and maintained by those charged with governance, management and other personnel, to provide **reasonable** assurance about the achievement of an entity's objectives with regard to the reliability of **financial reporting** effectiveness and efficiency of operations and compliance with applicable **laws and regulations**.

Task 3.1

	Accuracy	Classification	Cut-off	Existence
Date of the invoice			✓	
Description of the item purchased		✓		
Monetary amount	✓			

Task 3.2

	Increase	Decrease
An increase in the auditor's assessment of risk of misstatement	✓	
An increase in the use of other substantive procedures directed at the same assertion		✓
Stratification of the population being tested		✓

Task 3.3

	Test of control	Substantive procedure
Comparison of the current year's revenue figure with the previous year's figure		✓
Observation of the despatch procedures in respect of goods leaving an entity's warehouse	✓	
Vouching of an addition to non-current assets to the supplier's invoice		✓

Task 3.4

	Test data	Audit software
Comparison of the cost and net realisable value of inventory items to determine the lower value		✓
Input of data with false inventory code numbers to check that the system rejects such data	✓	
Extraction of inventory balances over £5,000 in order to carry out further testing		✓

Task 3.5

	Strong	Weak	No effect
Management is competent and acts with integrity	✓		
Management has not made an assessment of the risk of fraud		✓	

Task 4.1

	Flowchart	Questionnaire	Checklist
A listing of controls necessary to provide reasonable assurance of effective internal control within a given transaction cycle			✓
A pictorial presentation of the processing steps within a given transaction cycle	✓		

Task 4.2

	True	False
Working papers are prepared by the external auditor because there is a legal requirement to do so		✓
The objective of working papers is to provide evidence that the audit was planned and performed in accordance with International Standards on Auditing	✓	
Working papers should contain the name of who performed the audit work and the date it was performed	✓	

External Auditing (Skills)

Task 1.1

   (c)   Sales, purchases and payroll

Task 1.2

	Increase	Decrease
The allocation of responsibilities so that different personnel are responsible for the authorisation, processing and recording of transactions		✓
Management has a positive attitude and discipline towards controls and their enforcement		✓
The accounting staff are inexperienced and have a poor understanding of accounting principles	✓	

Task 1.3

Internal control procedure	Risk mitigated
Purchase invoices matched to goods received records prior to posting to the ledger	Paying for goods not received
Physical counts of inventory and reconciliation with recorded amounts	Theft of inventory

Task 1.4

	Strength	Weakness
The computerised payroll is processed weekly by Amelia who is also responsible for amending the standing data details such as the addition of new employees and changes to wage rates.		✓
The managing director, David Delaware, reviews the BACS listing of net pay details per employee and signs the listing before authorising the assistant accountant, Marie, to transmit the details to the company's bank.	✓	

Task 1.5

	Understated	Overstated
Trade receivables has increased by 20% and revenue has increased by 5%		✓
Trade payables has decreased by 10% and purchases has decreased by 7%	✓	

Task 1.6

    (a)   **Non-current asset register**

    (b)   **Goods received records**

Task 1.7

    (i)   Payment 31 March 20X9 by cheque: **Post year-end bank statement**

    (ii)   Sales invoice 27 March 20X9 not accepted: **Goods returned note**

Task 1.8

(i)   **Risks**

- Inappropriate split between current and non-current liabilities

- Incomplete disclosure in the notes to the financial statements

- Going concern risk if company fails to comply with the terms of the loan

- Inflation of profits to ensure compliance with the interest cover requirement

(ii)   **Procedures**

- Inspect loan agreement for terms and conditions

- Direct confirmation with lender of balance outstanding at the year end

- Vouch loan repayments and interest to bank statements and cash book

- Re-perform the calculation of the split between current and non-current liabilities

- Inspect notes to the financial statements to ensure disclosures in respect of the terms are complete

- Examine cash flow forecasts to ensure loan obligations can be met in the future

- Examine profit forecasts to ensure interest cover can be maintained in the foreseeable future

Task 2.1

An overstatement of inventory amounting to £4,200, and an overstatement of receivables amounting to £3,800 **Requires to be adjusted.**

Task 2.2

- Vouch a sample of entries for materials to invoices

- Vouch a sample of entries for wages/salaries to payroll records

- Trace a sample of invoices to costing records

- Trace a sample of timesheet/payroll details to the costing records

- Re-perform the overhead percentage calculation

- For a sample of contracts in progress at the year end compare actual costs:

    –   To contract price to identify losses

    –   To budget to identify cost overruns and potential losses

Task 2.3

Refer to supervisor

Task 2.4

No further action

Task 3.1

(i) **Consequences**

■ Equipment recorded in the register may not exist or may have been stolen

■ Equipment in existence, acquisitions or disposals may not be recorded

■ Equipment may be fully written down but still in use

■ Equipment may be impaired and consequently overvalued

■ Depreciation charges on the equipment may be inappropriate

(ii) **Recommendations**

■ Periodic reconciliation of:

– Physical equipment to register to ensure completeness of recording

– Entries in the register to physical equipment to ensure existence and in good condition

■ Reconciliation to be performed independent of custodian

■ Differences to be reported and investigated

■ Monitoring of procedures to ensure checks undertaken

Task 3.2

(a) **Modified**

(b) **Not modified**

Task 3.3

(d) Your firm's money laundering reporting officer without discussion with Peter Nash

for your notes

for your notes